There is a tide in the affairs of men
Which, taken at the flood, leads on to fortune;
Omitted, all the voyage of their life
Is bound in shallows and in miseries.
On such a full sea are we now afloat,
And we must take the current when it serves,
Or lose our ventures.

William Shakespeare, The Tragedy of Julius Caesar

WHOLE EARTH?

ALIGNING HUMAN SYSTEMS AND NATURAL SYSTEMS

Mark Edwards
Lloyd Timberlake

HARD
RAIN
PROJECT

Published in Great Britain in 2012 by
Still Pictures Moving Words Ltd
199 Shooters Hill Road
London SE3 8UL, UK

A catalogue record for this book is available from the British Library

ISBN 978-1-905588-04-6

Design Bailey and Kenny
Managing editor Mark Reynolds
Scans by Andrew Jackson, Actpix Ltd
Image preparation by Stephen Johnson, Copyrightimage Ltd
Printed by Pureprint Group, Uckfield

Special thanks to Dag Jonzon, Swedish International Development Cooperation Agency (Sida), Peter Bennett, Rainforest Concern and Annemiek Hoogenboom and Clara Govier, People's Postcode Lottery. They made the *Whole Earth?* exhibition possible.

I also want to thank Joan Walley MP, Chair of the Environmental Audit Committee for her support and encouragement and for talking the message to a new audience.

Mark Edwards

Contents

Roadmap to a sustainable future

Bob Dylan's song, "A Hard Rain's A-Gonna Fall" inspired this book and exhibition. I had the idea to illustrate each line of the lyrics, and for thirty years I travelled around the world on assignments that allowed me to capture the photographs that turn Dylan's prophetic words into images of the real world. Over the years I replaced many of my own images with pictures by friends and colleagues. Our photographs partner with Dylan's eerily beautiful lyrics to bring global challenges alive in a memorable way.

Some 15 million people on every continent have seen the Hard Rain exhibition since its launch at the Eden Project in May 2006. It has attracted many comments and much support from political and environmental leaders across the world. Even more rewarding are emails from people who have not previously engaged with the environmental debate.

Whole Earth? Aligning human systems and natural systems responds to their requests that we show solutions to the problems highlighted in Hard Rain. Lloyd Timberlake sets out the technologies, lifestyle approaches and development strategies that are available – if we choose sustainable development. It's a big if.

I once saw a homeless man in the early hours of a freezing cold morning in London take off his jeans to feed the fire he sat beside. I was with a friend who was wearing two pairs of trousers; he immediately took off the outer layer and gave them to the homeless man. A wonderful gesture, but this way of thinking won't solve the problems we now face. Habitat loss, population, peak oil around the corner, water stress and global warming are problems that demand a radically new worldwide approach, not gestures.

The question for visitors to this exhibition: is there public support for the long-term measures to tackle all our problems together? Will enough people find ways to show political leaders that there are votes for sustainable development? It will take a huge, prolonged popular uprising to save our civilization.

Mark Edwards
London, March 2012

Clockwise from top left:
Royal Botanic Gardens, Kew
Lalbagh Botanical Garden, Bangalore
Sida exhibition for the EU Committee of the Regions, Malmö (x2)
St Martin-in-the-Fields, Trafalgar Square, London
UN headquarters, New York
Royal Botanic Garden Edinburgh

The tasks ahead

Fifty years ago when Bob Dylan wrote "A Hard Rain's A-Gonna Fall" the Cuban missile crisis and the threat of nuclear oblivion hung over the world. Dylan said the lines were all beginnings of other songs he thought he would never live to write.

Today Hard Rain speaks to us not of bombs but of other types of planetary death. And it's not the future; it's now. Dylan's song connects dissimilar, strange things: sad forests, dead oceans, broken tongues, guns and sharp swords. So too today: all our problems, all our solutions, are connected.

You know about water scarcity, dwindling forests, extinctions, acid oceans, overfishing, hunger, poverty and that crossroads of all challenges: climate change…

Now think where those ever-accelerating trends will put the present generation of students in the coming decades. Before 2050, the world population will increase by 2 or 3 billion. Incomes will increase almost threefold; the demand for food and goods and energy and shelter will surge.

Now, put us and nature together, and the tasks ahead become obvious: we have to align human systems and natural systems to create a whole earth.

- Get the carbon out of energy systems while bringing electricity to all.

- Adapt to the climate change and sea-level rise that is already unavoidable.

- Build or rebuild cities to make them super-efficient for the 6–7 billion people who will live in them by 2050.

- Produce twice as much food as today without using any more land or water; doing it in ways that bring dignity to the billions who will still be living on farms and in rural villages.

- Use water efficiently (or by 2050, some 4.5 billion could be living in countries chronically short of water).

- Preserve the ecosystems that make life on earth possible.

- Kick the *stuff* out of progress: do more with less. People have used as much material (metal, wood, plastic) in the past fifty years as in all previous human history.

- Create the chance of satisfactory jobs or livelihoods for 9+ billion.

- Give everyone the possibility of safe, efficient housing.

- Provide healthcare for all.

- Redefine *prosperity*. Redefine *living well*.

- Increase empathy, so that people understand and identify with one another globally.

- Rebuild democracy so that when voters vote for sustainable development it will make a difference.

Now read on…

We have many of the technologies and lifestyle approaches needed to create a sustainable civilization; we are working on others. The question is: is there the political will to build and spread these budding solutions? It will be a wrenching change, and most of us who live them are comfortable with our carbon-based lifestyles. It will take leadership from the top by politicians, business and NGO leaders. And it will take a grassroots leadership to create the bottom-up movement required to maintain the resolve of decision-makers.

Car dump, Montana, USA
© David Woodfall/Hard Rain Picture Library

Reinvent the modern world

So-called global warming is just a secret ploy by wacko tree-huggers to make America energy independent, clean our air and water, improve the fuel efficiency of our vehicles, kick-start 21st-century industries, and make our cities safer and more liveable. Don't let them get away with it!

Chip Giller, grist.org

The climate is changing because human and natural systems are out of synch. Climate change alters water availability, degrades ecosystems, destroys biodiversity, and acidifies oceans. Right now it is killing and impoverishing people in the poorest countries, who have contributed least to the problem. It could cut unirrigated farm yields by half in many African countries by 2020 – a vast human disaster a historic eyeblink away. It makes poor people poorer: Inuit, who can no longer hunt on the ice the way they have for centuries, and Sahelian farmers south of the Sahara, who find it too hot and dry to keep farming. Extreme weather events are increasing in the rich countries, causing huge property damage and loss of harvests.

There is no single "solution", but there are thousands of solutions: small individual acts; big government policy changes; radically new forms of global governance and co-operation; new and renewable energy systems; cap-and-trade systems to establish a high price for carbon; new technology standards; new technology. We'll need them all. Changed human minds must drive these and other changes toward a new world of human activity and human living everywhere. All countries are "developing countries" now, needing to develop new, lower-carbon ways of heating, air-conditioning, moving around, manufacturing, farming and prospering.

Global carbon dioxide emissions continue to rise, threatening to create more climate- and heat-related disasters. The onslaught of floods, droughts, wildfires, windstorms, blizzards and tornadoes that hit the US in 2011 were part of the ongoing increase in US disasters and "a harbinger of things to come," said the head of the US National Oceanic and Atmospheric Administration. How ironic that the endless quest to fill our lives with comfort and happiness may create a world without either.

Austfonna ice cap, Svalbard archipelago, Norway
© Michael S. Nolan/Robert Harding Specialist Stock

13

A web of energy

It is clear that we must shift from carbon energy – coal, oil and gas – to renewable energies: solar, wind, hydro, wave, geothermal. Yet even those who agree with this truth like to argue about which energy is best; some champion solar, some wind, etc. That misses the point. Each has its strengths and weaknesses. So the goal is to create vast networks – electricity grids – that make the best of all the renewable energies.

The global consulting firm PwC – not an environmental NGO – has offered "a vision of Europe, in combination with countries in North Africa, developing an integrated power grid with 100% of electricity generation coming from renewable sources by 2050." Its roadmap of how to get there is based on "an evolutionary development mainly of the economical, legal and regulatory framework and does not require fundamental technological breakthroughs."

While this "supergrid" would depend to a great extent on solar power from North Africa, it would use renewable energy from everywhere: "Wind generation in the windy North Sea region, concentrating solar power (CSP) with storage in the sunny south, biomass and wind in the Baltic Sea region and Eastern Europe, and hydro in the mountainous regions of Scandinavia and the Alps." (Greenpeace has done its own, strikingly similar report calling for such a grid, and there are plans for others in other parts of the world.)

Most of the technical components for 100% renewable electricity are available in principle today. The economic costs to society of restructuring the energy system in this way would be small – at most, a few percentage points of gross domestic product over the coming decades. So why haven't countries done it already?

The 2050 vision requires simultaneous and coordinated progress on many fronts – including finance, technology, research and development, improved supply chains and increased grid capability. Above all, policy-makers will need to rewrite existing legislation to change the rules and incentives guiding participants in the energy market.

But what about bridging the gap between where we are now and that 2050 all-renewable vision? Two technologies, both controversial, could help. Nuclear power is a proven low-carbon energy source, but safety concerns were reignited by the cooling-system failures at Fukushima after the 2011 earthquake in Japan. The costs of decommissioning plants will be huge. The environmental movement is divided on whether nuclear should be a stepping-stone toward a renewable future. However, the last thirty years have shown that coal-fired power is the world's biggest killer. The coal industry believes carbon can be "captured" from power station smokestacks and stored indefinitely – but at great cost and using lots of water.

Natural gas is replacing coal to generate electricity in many countries. For an equivalent amount of heat, burning natural gas produces about 45% less CO_2 than coal. Increased demand for gas has led to higher prices, and attention has turned to shale gas. This too is controversial, with some studies suggesting the extraction and use of shale gas may pollute groundwater, and result in the release of more greenhouse gases than conventional natural gas. Do the negatives outweigh the positives?

Read more and join the debate:
www.hardrainproject.com/web_of_energy
www.hardrainproject.com/feedback

Biomass
Geothermal
Hydro
Ocean
Solar
Wind

This diagram shows how a full range of renewable energy sources can be interlinked via a "supergrid" across Europe and North Africa connecting large power plants with energy users over long distances. This is underpinned by "smart grid" technologies that enable two-way communication between energy producers and users to increase efficiency.

The renewable power mix is geographically optimized, with wind generation in the North Sea region, concentrating solar power (CSP) in the south, biomass and wind in the Baltic Sea region and Eastern Europe, and hydro in Scandinavia and the Alps.

The diagram does not indicate the contribution of decentralized renewable energy (solar roofs and small wind and biomass plants generating power close to where it is used), which could provide energy at a lower cost than the centralized grid – without the dependability and security risks associated with large-scale wind farms and imported energy from North Africa.

Satellite image © Qinetiq/Hard Rain Picture Library. Diagram © Michael Robinson/Hard Rain Picture Library

In May 2011, under pressure from voters, the German government announced plans to abandon nuclear energy completely by 2022. Increased investment in natural gas plants would provide a backup to ensure consistent supply for those times when solar, wind and hydroelectric sources did not meet demand.

Brokdorf nuclear power plant, Germany
© Reinhard Janke/Argus

Energy for all

Societies cannot develop without electricity. Yet so many people do without it. In Africa, only about 20% of people have direct access to electricity, and in some countries it is only 5%. Even in Africa's cities, electrification rates are lower than on any other continent. Yet there are also millions in Asia and Latin America who work by daylight and firelight.

Solutions here may never rely on grids, given vast distances and low population densities. Villages and homes may need isolated solar cells, biogas digesters and wind turbines. It may require new and improved technologies, but it will certainly need new partnerships among governments, companies and citizens' groups to disseminate the technologies.

Read more:
www.hardrainproject.com/energy_for_all

Cleaning solar panels in Waat village, Sudan
© Hartmut Schwarzbach/Hard Rain Picture Library

17

Super-efficient homes

Architects and developers understand we can no longer build leaky, badly insulated homes that cost huge sums to heat and cool. Many new homes today are built airtight and with new technologies for providing thermal insulation. Ventilation comes from pumping new air into the house, and the heat from the stale air leaving the building is captured. Houses built to the *Passivhaus* standard don't need central heating systems, even in cold countries, while an *Activhaus* is one that produces more energy than it consumes.

Only a tiny fraction of the housing stock is replaced each year. Improving the standards of new housing will do little to lower emissions from existing buildings. Countries like Germany, Denmark and Canada have introduced low-cost financing and other incentives to help encourage effective eco-refurbishments. Hundreds of thousands of homes are being improved each year, cutting emissions by several tonnes and dramatically reducing heating bills.

Read more:
www.hardrainproject.com/super-efficient_homes

Even building professionals tend to overestimate the costs of energy-efficient buildings, and underestimate the contribution of the built environment to climate change. Thus in many countries – including the US and UK – builders and developers lobby against improved building codes, so that even new buildings waste a lot of energy.

Sunlight House, Pressbaum, Vienna, Austria
(Hein-Troy Architekten/The VELUX Group)
© Adam Mork/Arcaid Images

Population: numbers and appetites

Some argue there are too many people on the planet. This is partly true; 7 billion is too many given the primitive technologies in use, from three-stone cooking fires to internal combustion, fossil-fuel engines. Education and reproductive health programmes can help stabilize population growth. This would also help reduce poverty and increase human potential. But since the mid-1990s, population has been a neglected issue. It is time to educate and empower women.

Others argue that how people live counts more than their numbers. Only 5% of the global population live in the US, but they produce a quarter of the world's CO_2 emissions. And, unlike Europe, the population of the US is growing fast – from 200 million in 1970 to over 303 million today, projected at 420 million in 2050.

Since 1950, the richest fifth of humanity has doubled its consumption of energy, meat, timber, steel and copper, and quadrupled its car ownership, while the poorest fifth of humanity has hardly increased its general consumption at all. The big increases in consumption now happen in countries such as China and India, which together are expected to add half a billion more people to the planet's population by 2050.

More than three-quarters of the world's people live in nations where national consumption has outstripped their countries' biological capacity. The wealthier among us must find ways to live within planetary means: renewable energy; efficient heating, cooling, and transport; diets that need less land and water.

Most population growth will take place in poorer nations, with some large countries such as Pakistan and Nigeria on course to triple their numbers by 2050. Such nations may need to skip the "big grids" of the industrialized nations and go straight to cell phones and local energy, water and sewerage solutions. Whether it is numbers, reproductive rates or appetites, population is about what people know and how they live.

Read more:
www.hardrainproject.com/population

Over-consumers in rich countries blame "over-breeders" in poor countries for the planet's ills, but the rich minority use the equivalent per person of three or even five planets. The key challenges of this century are to live and consume within planetary means, empower women to have as few children as they want and keep them alive and thriving, and to help billions of people out of poverty and toward safe, fulfilled and dignified lives. Imagine a third picture, in which the amount of possessions is "just right". Would there be a car, two cars, or only bicycles? A computer per person? A TV per person? How must both appetites and technologies change so that 9 billion people can live within the means of our small planet?

The Namgay family, Bhutan (*above*) and the Skeen Family, USA (*below*) display their household possessions
© Peter Menzel

Meeting the needs of all

The planet is too small and interconnected for the rich to be comfortable and secure while billions suffer poverty.

Poverty is disastrous for people and the planet. Over three billion people, almost half the world population, live on less than $2.50 a day; and more than four-fifths live in countries where the income gap between the rich and poor is widening. Aside from being a personal tragedy, poverty can keep people from taking part in solutions – for themselves or their societies. The only way poor people can adapt to climate change is through having sufficient income, savings, insurance and mobility.

Governments cannot solve poverty, but they can set up the conditions whereby people can pull themselves out of penury: access to credit and education for all; enforcing fair laws fairly; streamlining bureaucracies; and creating effective safety nets for the poorest. Poor-country governments would be helped in this effort if all the richer countries kept their promises: to establish a global trade regime that helps countries trade out of poverty; to increase aid; and to help poorer countries adapt to climate change.

Read more:
www.hardrainproject.com/meeting_the_needs

Meeting the needs of all would require spectacular global co-operation to rebuild capitalism, financial markets and trade regimes to make it possible. This is hard to imagine when so many governments, rich and poor, are today so ineffectual, short-sighted, divided and in the control of business and markets.

Illegally logged hard wood, Nigeria
© Mark Edwards/Hard Rain Picture Library

'Systematizing' cities

In 2008, for the first time in history, more than half the global population lived in cities. By 2030, some 5 billion will live in cities, and by 2050 that could rise to 7 billion. In Africa and Asia, the number of city dwellers is expected to double from 2000 levels by 2030.

No country has developed economically without urbanizing. People who move to cities have fewer children than those who remain in the countryside. But today's cities tend to sprawl unplanned across the landscape, particularly in the poorer parts of the planet, where newcomers build huts and shanties on dangerous land, where it is hard to bring in services such as sewerage and electricity.

Cities must be planned more systematically and holistically to take advantage of economies of scale and limit their ecological footprints – easier to do when people live closer together. This means building smart transport networks, in which cars, trains, subways, bikes and walkways are all part of one interconnected system. It means using combined heat and power, recycling water and wastes, and bringing nature into cities – in parks, gardens, city farms and reserves. The systemic approaches required are not just a question of mechanics and infrastructure, but also of human behaviour and political systems. Many of the solutions will involve allowing slum dwellers and new arrivals to participate more in planning city growth.

Read more:
www.hardrainproject.com/systematizing_cities

Bangladesh has grown from a town of 300,000 people in the 1950s to a megacity of over 12 million, and its infrastructure is inadequate, weak and unreliable. Kuala Lumpur, by contrast, is developing an interconnected, state-of-the-art public transport system.

Above: Dhaka, Bangladesh
© Mark Edwards/Hard Rain Picture Library

Below: Kuala Lumpur, Malaysia
© Nico Stengert/IB/Lineair

Housing people

Question: how to house the 9 billion people of 2050, when today 1 billion people are homeless or living in bad shelters? Answer: in every sustainable way possible, depending on culture, climate, environment and other local conditions.

Homelessness is mainly a majority world challenge, but millions are homeless in Europe and North America too. In these regions, empty houses and flats are available, but the homeless are too poor to buy or rent them and cannot get credit. Yet housing policy is tricky; the recession of the first decade of this century was partly caused by irresponsibly offered housing credit.

Other policies besides appropriate credit will involve reclaiming and retrofitting the derelict housing stock of urban centres, helping people build their own homes, developing new forms of group housing, and putting housing where people can use it conveniently and safely without cars. All this will need clever financing and public/private partnerships

Some old forms of housing are becoming modern. Mud has been a building material since before the Iron Age; it is now a building material for the rich in some parts of the US. It, and new forms of mud bricks, are being "redeveloped" for building use in much of Asia and Africa. Recycled glass and plastic are being used elsewhere, and wood is making a strong return. The challenge is not building the houses, but getting people into homes.

Read more:
www.hardrainproject.com/housing_people

The magic of squatter cities is that they are improved steadily and gradually, increment by increment, by the people living there. Each home is built that way, and so is the whole community.

Buenos Aires ten years ago (*left*)... and now
© Mark Edwards/Hard Rain Picture Library

Future farming

Given the numbers of hungry people alive today, feeding the 9+ billion people of 2050 will require a doubling of present food production levels. This calls for new hardware and new "software" – in the form of educating farmers for a new sustainable Green Revolution. Governments need to put more effort into agricultural research and abolish the perverse subsidies that help the world's richest farmers better compete against the poorest in Africa and Asia. All farmers need access to credit, markets and crop insurance.

Future farming cannot afford to waste water, land, living species or human labour. New technologies will be needed to get the most out of every bit of topsoil and every drop of water, along with new crop varieties to cope with extreme and changing climate. Does this mean controversial genetically-modified organisms? Perhaps in places it does, as large parts of Africa lack sufficient organic material for an organic approach.

Breakthroughs in technology are required to manage salty and acidic soils and to get plant roots to absorb more nitrogen and thus need less fertilizer. Methods of planting and harvesting using less machinery and energy must also be developed. Much land has been ruined by agriculture. This land will have to be reclaimed, and more farming be done in odd places, like city rooftops. And all this must be accomplished while adding to, rather than diminishing, the biodiversity and ecosystem services that make farming possible in the first place.

Read more:
www.hardrainproject.com/future_farming

Fierce arguments rage about how to grow more food for more people. Can we expand farmland (without destroying key ecosystems such as rainforests)? Should we redouble efforts to create a new Green Revolution? (Perhaps one with fewer artificial fertilizers and pesticides than the first one.) Should agricultural systems embrace only biotechnology, or become only organic? As usual the answer is probably a synthesis of all methods and technologies, without damaging ecosystems. We need now the greenest of revolutions.

Exhibition to promote industrial agriculture, USA, 1930
© SVT-Bild

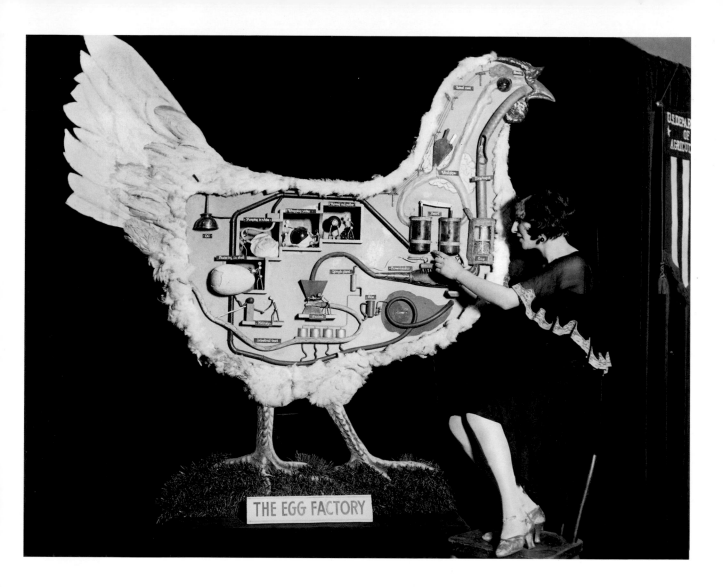

THE EGG FACTORY

Water: scarce, cheap and wasted

Our planet probably has no more and no less water than it has ever had, but many more people use much more of it. Today, a billion people cannot get enough safe drinking water.

By 2050, 45% of humankind will live in countries chronically short of water. Water is scarce – but cheap (or free). It is valuable – but wasted and polluted. It is the stuff of life, but dirty water spreads disease: bad water and poor sanitation kill 5,000 children a day. Climate change is moving the available fresh water to different places, and new water systems are required to obtain it.

The biggest industrial use of water is for cooling thermal power stations, and carbon capture and storage systems would require vast amounts of water – two more reasons to move from carbon energy to renewable energy.

Two-thirds of all the water taken from nature is used to grow crops. This dries the landscape, empties wetlands, destroys fisheries and even alters the climate.

There are myriad solutions, both big and small. Sanitation systems that use little or no water are available. Drip irrigation, rather than flooding fields, can cut water use by 60% or more. Some Indian farmers make their own drip systems from plastic sleeves made to hold popsicles. If farmers are taught how to measure and evaluate their water use, they learn to use less of it. And effective water pricing can help people and businesses understand its value.

Many small dams are usually more effective than a few big dams, both in terms of irrigation and hydropower. Water use must be systematized overall, as it has been in Singapore, where domestic water use has fallen in the last decade since the introduction of water tariffs and low-use taps and toilets.

Living things need water. Let's use it carefully.

Read more:
www.hardrainproject.com/water

Children jumping into a pond during
a break in the monsoon, Bangladesh
© Gil Moti/Still Pictures

The problem of stuff

Where human consumption differs from that of every other creature on the planet is that it doesn't sit easily within nature's cycles.

Julie Hill

In the past fifty years, humans have consumed more resources – or stuff – than in all previous history. At the beginning of the 1900s, some 40% of the stuff used in the wealthier parts of the world was renewable – farm, fishery or forestry products – but by the end of that century the figure was below 10%, with the majority of materials now made from metals and minerals or derived from fossil fuels.

Between 1970 and 1995, the US consumed about one-third of the materials used globally (despite having only 5% of its population), and today providing US citizens with products requires the extraction of more than 25,000 pounds (11,000 kilogrammes) of new non-fuel minerals per person each year. This pursuit of materials damages habitats, biodiversity, fisheries and farmland.

We need to develop new design standards for the stuff around us, so that everything we buy reflects mounting environmental pressures. Imagine a world in which all energy is renewable; all gadgets are designed to generate their own energy; all products are designed to last longer, and to be easily recycled at the end of their useful lives. A world where all materials can either be circulated in the economy indefinitely, or returned to nature's cycles. A world where our natural desires for novelty and the enjoyment of stuff are met in ways that are compatible with a world of 9+ billion people. Imagine a world where we design out waste, and design in a secure future. If we don't ask for that world, we won't get it.

Read more:
www.hardrainproject.com/stuff

Eliminate waste. Make things recyclable and biodegradable. But that won't be enough. Our crowded planet will require a change away from recreational consumption and measuring self-worth in terms of the ownership of things. Who is going to preach that message? Who is going to listen?

Computers in a skip, London
© Ceanne Jansen/Hard Rain Picture Library

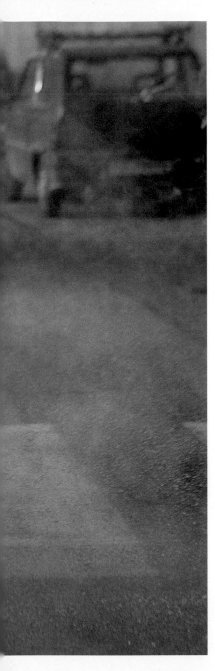

Costing the earth: changing the rules

Every time a group – whether economists, government bureaucrats or business people – sits down to decide how to encourage the planet toward sustainable progress, they end up calling for "full-cost pricing". This means that the price we pay should reflect a good's or a service's full cost – including social and environmental costs. The price of petrol should include the cost of sending armies to the Middle East. The price of coal-fired electricity should include the costs of the premature deaths caused by its pollution – and its mining.

Including such costs would not only better reflect reality (an alleged goal of economics), but also make renewable energy much more cost-effective than fossil fuels. (This approach is also called "internalizing externalities" – the mild, technical word "externalities" referring to things like extinctions and environmental destruction.)

Sustainable human progress also requires tax shifts: that is, we stop taxing things we like, such as jobs and investments in new technologies, and start taxing things we don't, such as waste and pollution. Such taxes also encourage companies to keep improving, which laws requiring minimum standards do not.

If these steps are so logical, why haven't they been taken? Because powerful industries oppose them; because government bureaucrats do not like change; and because we the voters have not demanded them.

Read more:
www.hardrainproject.com/costing_the_earth

Pollution costs lives, particularly the lives of the young, the old and the infirm. This is one of the biggest costs omitted from the prices we pay for energy, transport and goods produced in dirty factories.

Children protest against traffic pollution, Italy
© A. Doto/UNEP/Hard Rain Picture Library

The web of life

Growing numbers of people and their increasing consumption mean fewer resources for wild plants and animals: less land, less water, and changes in the climates they evolved in. Extinctions are rippling through the 30 million species thought to exist (about 2 million of which have been identified).

It is not just the destruction of habitat – land, oceans, lakes and rivers – but also the moving of plants and animals; these invasive species become causes of extinctions. More important than individual species are the networks – the ecosystems – that support them, support life on earth, and provide us with food, water, topsoil and fibres. The most complex ecosystems containing the greatest species diversity tend to be in the tropics, where nations are poorer and populations are growing fastest.

It is impossible to put a monetary value on ecosystem services such as forests' and oceans' ability to lock up carbon and keep it out of the atmosphere, but when scientists try, they come up with figures far larger than global economies. This truth ought to help us figure ecosystem services into our financial and economic planning, budgeting far more for investments in conservation, investments that will begin to pay off immediately and will be ever more important to larger, future generations.

Read more:
www.hardrainproject.com/web_of_life

Sustainability means that human society can continue to exist because ecosystems are able to go on providing life-sustaining services such as clean water, soil fertility, climate regulation, etc. But today most indicators are moving in the wrong direction. We are overusing and/or misusing two-thirds of our major ecosystem services.

Clearcut logging, Washington State, USA
© Daniel Dancer/Hard Rain Picture Library

Human rights:
the foundation of it all

There are two ways of looking at human rights issues in terms of aligning human and natural systems: negative and positive.

The negative view asks what is the point of creating a sustainable planet upon which the rights of millions are denied on the basis of gender, religion, ethnic or national origins or sexual preference?

A more positive approach starts with the frequently stated view that sustainability cannot be achieved without the effective, popular participation of all in decision-making. The real environmental decision-makers are not governments but voters, the same people who also decide on a daily basis how to get rid of garbage, how to transport themselves and how much water to use.

Sustainable progress not only requires broad participation, it requires that individuals and the organizations they form have the right to be consulted in decision-making, the right to the information required to make good decisions, and the right to legal remedies and redress when their health and their environment has been or may be seriously effected.

These are the human rights that form the basis of sustainable human and planetary development.

Read more:
www.hardrainproject.com/human_rights

In much of the rural majority world, women do most of the farm work, while men make most of the decisions. The men are usually listed as owning the land, but they often work elsewhere. So when government agents come calling with a training programme or credit scheme, they ignore the women running the farms because their names are not on government lists. Yet throughout the majority world, women are taking greater control of their lives and livelihoods.

Women at a village meeting, India
© Mark Edwards/Hard Rain Picture Library

The great migration

No regions are immune to climate change, but it will affect different places in different ways. Or maybe not. The 1930s Dust Bowl of the US western plains looked a lot like what has been happening in Africa over recent decades. And the 2011 drought across the southern US states looked a lot like the Dust Bowl.

In the 1930s, western US farmers were already over-farming their land due to pressure from falling farm prices. When drought struck, wind took their topsoil away; many farmers – one in ten in some regions – had to abandon their farms and take to the road.

In the mid-1980s, farmers in over 20 African nations were over-farming their land due to pressure from falling farm prices. When drought struck, wind took their topsoil away; many farmers, 10 million by most estimates, had to abandon their farms and take to the road.

Read more:
www.hardrainproject.com/the_great_migration

Migrant mother and child, Nipomo, California, 1936
© Dorothea Lange/FSA

A swarm to the cities

A lot of US farmers fled into the slums and tenements of the big cities in the 1930s, just as many African farmers are today fleeing to the slums of Africa's big cities – and Europe's.

But it is not just Africans; the world has been moving into cities. Now for the first time in history more people are urban than are rural. By 2050, 6–7 billion people will live in cities, about as many as live on the entire planet today.

Human civilization is changing. The hunter-gatherers who became farmers are now halfway down the road from being agriculturists to becoming urbanites. These migrants move in hope from field to favela.

Read more:
www.hardrainproject.com/squatter_cities

American farming families in the 1930s; and people in Ethiopia in the present day. Over-farming and drought led to erosion on both continents and created a huge wave of migration to the cities.

Top: Fleeing a dust storm, Cimarron County, Oklahoma, 1936
© Arthur Rothstein/FSA

Bottom: Dust storm, Borkena valley, Wollo region, Ethiopia
© Mark Edwards/Hard Rain Picture Library

When the soil leaves the land so do the people.

Toward Los Angeles, California, 1937
© Dorothea Lange/FSA

Slums and shantytowns are both wonderful and horrible places.

They are wonderful in that they do not give hard, important work to small children, such as tending poultry or herding sheep; so urban children are more likely to go to school. And because children are not so economically important to their parents, urban parents tend to have fewer of them. Large agrarian families give way to small urban ones, putting an end to a major theme of human history, continuous population growth. Families build their own homes, and work with other families to build their own neighbourhoods; there is energy and originality.

These are the neighbourhoods where the transition from poverty occurs, where the next middle class is forged, where the next generation's dreams, movements and governments are created. These are the places where the next great cultural boom will be born.

Two billion people – a third of humanity – are currently moving from rural to urban living.

Migrant families living on the outskirts of Mexico City
© Mark Edwards/Hard Rain Picture Library

Left: Children on their way to school, Cité Soleil squatter city, Port-au-Prince, Haiti
© Mark Edwards/Hard Rain Picture Library

Social cohesiveness is the crucial factor differentiating "slums of hope" from "slums of despair". This is where community-based organizations (CBOs) and NGOs shine. Typical CBOs include community theatre and leisure groups; sports groups; residents' associations or societies; savings and credit groups; childcare groups; minorities' support groups; clubs; advocacy groups; and more. CBOs as interest associations have filled an institutional vacuum, providing basic services such as communal kitchens, milk for children, income-earning schemes and co-operatives.

More than 90% of enterprises in developing countries are small businesses and provide jobs for millions of people. The Dharavi slum, Mumbai's largest, has 4,000 recycling units employing 30,000 rag pickers; 6,000 tons of rubbish are sorted in the slum every day.

Small enterprises tend to be highly innovative, make excellent use of scarce capital and skills, and provide a range of services and goods both to their communities and to large corporations.

Read more:
www.hardrainproject.com/cbos_and_ngos

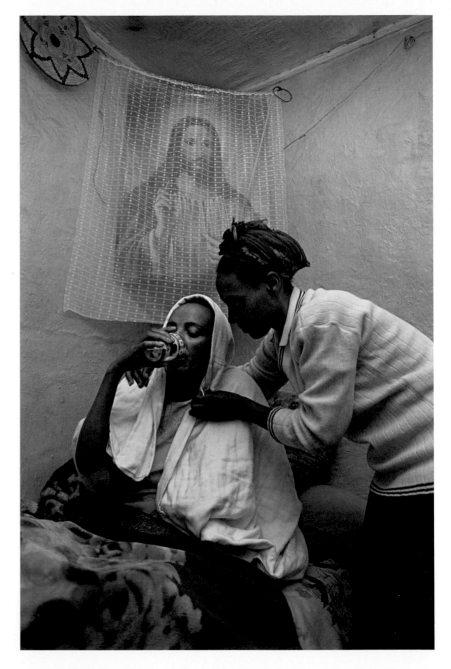

Left: Volunteer health workers weighing a baby and attending a home delivery, Mexico City

Right: HIV-positive carer looks after a patient dying from AIDS, Addis Ababa, Ethiopia

All© Mark Edwards/Hard Rain Picture Library

Left: Itinerant salesman, Mexico City
Top right: Recycling unit, Dharavi slum, Mumbai
Bottom right: Food stall, Malaysia
All © Mark Edwards/Hard Rain Picture Library

Above: Shop signs, Ouagadougou, Burkina Faso
Right: Carnival in a squatter city, Brazil
All © Mark Edwards/Hard Rain Picture Library

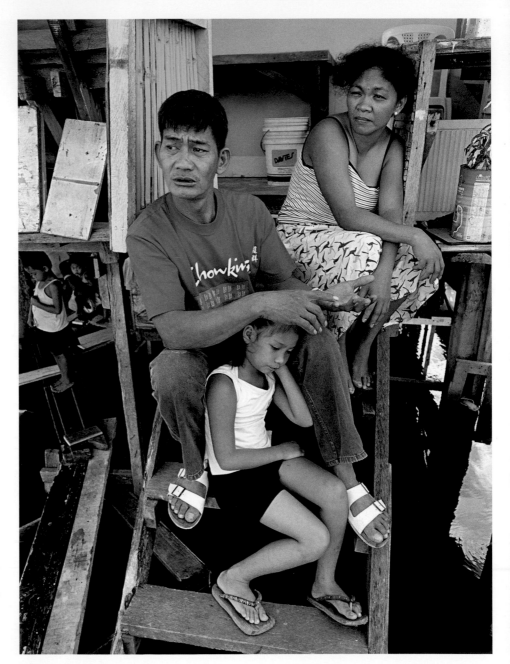

In many coastal cities, families too poor to buy homes inland with access to clean water are forced to build makeshift houses along estuaries which are frequently flooded. There is no sanitation system and rubbish and sewage is dumped in the water.

Squatter families, Cebu City, Philippines
© Mark Edwards/Hard Rain Picture Library

But it is easy to romanticize slums and shantytowns. The latter are built where land is available, which often means dangerous land, prone to flooding or mudslides. So cities cannot be planned. It is harder to provide roads, transport, sewerage, and other services. Building "illegally", new arrivals may not want to be on government censuses. So governments cannot plan for their needs. Nor can they plan adequate protection from the ravages of climate change. Some cities offer much more opportunity for upward mobility than others; few African cities are ready – in terms of jobs, schools and virtually all other needs – to accept the numbers arriving every year.

The goal is to align the energy and organization of the slum and shanty dwellers with the best of enlightened urban government. There are good examples of such alignments all over the world. But they are rare, for many reasons, perhaps the most important being that neither side trusts the other.

And those who stay behind

The other side of the urban-rural coin is that by 2050, some 2–3 billion people will remain in the world's rural villages and on its farms, growing food and fibre for the vast city populations. To fulfil this heroic task, they will need all the best of all modern technologies – electricity, internet, transport, healthcare, housing, storage facilities, refrigeration – all the things that so much of the rural majority world lacks today.

They will have to adapt their farming to the changes and disasters that climate change is bringing. No matter how big the drought or flood, the effects are always local, hitting individuals, families and villages. All disasters are local. So the solutions must be forms of local development that help individuals and families cope: jobs, income, credit, insurance, healthcare and transport.

The US Dust Bowl was a time of misery for small farmers, but many could leave and find jobs, could get credit and various forms of help from state or national programmes.

The challenge today is to connect national and international aid agencies, UN agencies and the World Bank to the local level, with national governments acting as partners to both sides as intermediaries and honest brokers. All the energy and all the knowledge are at that local level – whether in Latin American shantytowns, remote African farms, or Pacific villages on tiny atolls. If that energy and knowledge can be encouraged by outside resources, people will be able to cope, and maybe even to thrive. Peasant farmers won't feed the future billions. Neither will unsustainable, carbon-based industrial farming.

Read more:
www.hardrainproject.com/rural

Niftine Sawadogo feeding her newborn baby,
Kalsaka village, Yatenga Province, Burkina Faso
© Mark Edwards/Hard Rain Picture Library

People are already adapting. In Burkina Faso long, low lines of stones have been erected to control the run-off of rare rains and guide it to crops. Trees are being planted all across the Sahel – that dry band across Africa between the Sahara and the more humid regions – to decrease the erosion and drying effects of strong winds. Tree crops also supply nourishment for mothers, babies and children if crops fail, improve their diet throughout the year, and provide a lasting source of income for African families that helps send children to school and pays for their healthcare. Protected forests are more valuable to villagers than the timber they could provide if cut, and increasing tree cover stops villages being swallowed by the desert.

The internet can bring the world and its culture to rural children, but it can also bring training on specific, local forms of agriculture.

Left: A project worker shows farmers how lines of stones laid along level contours slow rainwater run-off

Right: Jean-Marie compares the millet and sorghum harvests from fields with and without stone lines

All © Mark Edwards/Hard Rain Picture Library

This water pump, installed with NGO
assistance, frees women from a 7-kilometre
walk to collect water from a pond.

Children collecting water in Kalsaka village
© Mark Edwards/Hard Rain Picture Library

Trees provide nourishment for mothers, babies and children, improve their diet, and provide a lasting source of income for African families to pay for schooling and healthcare.

Winnowing wheat, Burkina Faso
© Mark Edwards/Hard Rain Picture Library

The rural tropics are littered with broken-down tractors and other bits of machinery no local can maintain or repair. Aid-giving countries have tended to give what their companies make rather than what recipients really need. Often something like a foot-pedal water pump or a hand-cranked threshing machine can help farmers earn more than any tractor – at a fraction of the cost.

Abandoned bulldozer, Burkina Faso
© Mark Edwards/Hard Rain Picture Library

However, rural education need not depend on modern technology. A school founded by philosopher J. Krishnamurti in 1926 in India's Rishi Valley has become the hub of an expanding network of innovative "satellite schools" for surrounding villages. Contoured and planted with fruit trees, each school is a green public space, a village commons with facilities to serve the whole community – a place for village entertainment, adult education classes and a centre for preserving local biodiversity. The school developed a set of 500 story cards that promote ethnic harmony, sexual equality and love of the environment. Over 200,000 government and non-government schools throughout India have adopted this "school in a box" concept. It is also burgeoning across Africa, and is applicable to rural communities throughout the world.

Indigenous people

A lot of indigenous people live in important and threatened ecosystems: the Arctic, the Amazon and the High Andes, the remoter parts of Africa, the "tribal" lands of many Asian countries.

Everyone benefits when these ecosystems are protected and managed sustainably. By and large, indigenous people have done a fairly good job of their husbandry over the centuries. Sometimes they have failed by themselves – overusing natural resources or responding ineffectively to environmental damage – but usually their failures come when foreign "developers" intrude into their land and cultures.

Few governments have managed to figure out how to reward indigenous people for conservation services that benefit the rest of us, or how to encourage them to keep providing those services. There have been minor exceptions: local indigenous people getting a cut of the proceeds of a lodge or game reserve in their lands, or building trade through forestry.

The trick will be to come up with policies to help indigenous people to keep protecting their lands, their ecosystems – but also their cultures and languages, parts of humanity's shared adventure on earth that are disappearing all too rapidly.

Read more:
www.hardrainproject.com/indigenous_people

Yanomami mother breastfeeding her baby and an orphan monkey

© Mark Edwards/Hard Rain Picture Library

Getting personal

Nobody made a greater mistake than he who did nothing because he could do only a little.

Edmund Burke, orator, philosopher and MP (1729–1797)

What's the big idea?

What can any one person do? An infinite number of things, as it turns out. Many planet-saving activities are money-saving too; many are downright fun; many are both.

Doing the things we've been told to do for years – insulating our homes, adjusting thermostats in our homes and cars to reduce heating and cooling, and driving so as to improve fuel economy – all save money. But bicycling is more fun than driving, and saves more money and more carbon. The US environmentalist Stewart Brand argues that Californians are so green precisely because they are such hedonists.

Personalize your planet-saving. You may enjoy gardening, birdwatching or boating. Climate change is disrupting such activities as it changes rainfall patterns and natural habitats, and brings more storms, floods and droughts. Join or form a birding, boating or garden club.

Then write letters and emails to politicians, perhaps once a week, as an individual or an organization. Only turning off the lights when we leave the room won't do it. We need tough new policies, and politicians need the courage to implement them. Help them find that courage.

Join an environmental or sustainable development pressure group – a local, national or global one, or maybe one of each. That would increase and focus political pressure and also help you educate yourself and your friends and family.

But these are just suggestions. It's really up to you.

Read more:
www.hardrainproject.com/getting_personal

Families in the UK are spending £30 billion a year heating the planet directly. Insulating our homes will cut the national carbon footprint by 10%.

Thermal image of 10 Downing Street
© Graeme Robertson/Guardian News & Media Ltd

Choose Fairtrade

Changing the way we shop for coffee or tea, flowers or bananas, wine or spices, cosmetics or clothes means major improvements in the lives and livelihoods of farmers and workers in poorer countries.

Harriet Lamb, Executive Director, Fairtrade Foundation

Small farmers all over the world, but particularly in the majority world, are forced to sell their crops to middlemen or to big corporations at prices that are kept, by the buyers, as low as possible. Often there is little or no competition among buyers, or the farmers have poor or no knowledge of the global prices for their goods, so they cannot negotiate effectively.

Many Northern countries have movements to make these transactions fairer, to pay farmers prices that reflect the labour and efforts to improve quality they have put into growing and harvesting their crops. In many countries, it is the Fairtrade movement that does this.

This movement has shown the power that each and every one of us has to create change. In 2010, nine out of ten people in the UK bought a Fairtrade product, and globally some 7 million farmers, workers and their families are benefiting. It is a movement that is steadily gathering force.

People in the rich world are shocked when they hear that many growers still scrape by on less than $2 a day, or have to choose between putting a meal on the table at night or sending their kids to school in the morning. Faced with these facts, the public have shown their willingness to challenge such injustice. They have sent a message to companies that they want them to play fair by the farmers and workers who grow their food. Fairtrade puts producers right at the heart of trade. As one banana farmer said: "I used to just be someone who loaded boxes of bananas. In this new system, I am an international businessman."

Read more:
www.hardrainproject.com/fairtrade

Fairtrade banana plantation, Zambia
© Ron Giling/Lineair

Message in a bottle

Wrapping perishable vegetables in a material that can last 500 years in the ground just doesn't make any sense. We need to target packaging, rethink our buying habits and create more demand for positive change.

David de Rothschild, environmental campaigner and explorer

Almost all the plastic ever manufactured is still in the environment, and scientists estimate that at least a million seabirds and 100,000 marine mammals and sea turtles die every year as a direct result of plastic pollution. Aside from an astonishing 46,000 pieces of visible marine debris in every square mile of ocean, plastic that has degraded into microscopic particles secretes toxic chemicals into the sea and into the food chain, turning mussels and lugworms into sterile hermaphrodites.

Manufacturers are beginning to replace plastic packaging with biodegradable cornstarch and cellulose alternatives, but we can all lessen the impact by changing how we use, dispose of and reuse plastics. All types of plastic can be recycled six times and can then be burned to harvest the embedded energy, although incineration throws up its own environmental problems. Recycling the plastic we have already created keeps it out of landfill and the wider environment.

Sainsbury's may have urged customers to "take an old bag shopping", and most of the leading supermarkets are cutting down on single-use plastic bags, but all kinds of manufacturers and retailers still fall short when it comes to packaging.

Read more:
www.hardrainproject.com/message_in_a_bottle

Above: European white stork at a landfill site, Spain
© John Cancalosi/Hard Rain Picture Library

Right: Pelican, India
© Gidwani Mohan/UNEP

Salad days

Having one meat-free day a week is a meaningful change that everyone can make, that goes to the heart of several important political, environmental and ethical issues all at once. It not only addresses pollution, but better health, the ethical treatment of animals, global hunger, and community and political activism.

Paul McCartney

It takes a great deal of water to grow grain for livestock, and a great deal of energy to transport it. After eating it, sheep and cows give off a lot of methane, a much more powerful climate-changing gas than CO_2.

Too much meat is not good for us: it clogs our arteries, and helps make us fat. Governments in the wealthier countries are publishing guidelines suggesting people eat more fruits, vegetables and whole grains, and a lot less red meat. Celebrities offer similar calls: Paul McCartney and his family are backing their Meat Free Monday campaign.

In February 2011, the UK Government announced new health guidelines recommending that a balanced diet should contain no more than 1lb of red meat a week (about one steak and two pork chops). Meanwhile, the Food Standards Agency suggests that about 15% of our diet should come from protein-rich foods, which aside from meat and dairy products can include tofu, chickpeas, lentils, nuts and fish.

Whether it's beans on toast, pesto and pasta, dhal and rice, hummus and pitta or mackerel and salad, a protein-rich meal can be simple and tasty – and better for the planet.

Read more:
www.hardrainproject.com/food

Factory farm, Italy
© Mark Edwards/Hard Rain Picture Library

Where's the catch?

More than half the fish we eat in Britain comes from just three species – cod, tuna and salmon. You don't have to think too hard about that statistic to see the problem... At the same time, oily fish like sardines, anchovies, herring and mackerel are being industrially abused to feed pigs and chicken as well as salmon. Why aren't we eating them ourselves?

Hugh Fearnley-Whittingstall

Half of the world's fish stocks are fully exploited, and another quarter overfished – meaning populations are struggling to survive. In Europe, as much as 80% of stocks are overfished.

The biggest factor in the reduction in fish numbers is the massive advance in fishing technology over the last sixty years. Since 1950, the amount of fish caught worldwide has increased around fivefold.

Consumers in the UK tend to eat a small number of familiar favourites like cod. We ignore many of the fish that have nourished us for centuries. Paradoxically, increases in the size of trawls, nets and lines mean that alongside this narrowing of tastes, it has become harder for fishermen to discriminate between fish we want and fish we don't. This means bigger bycatches of non-target species, which are thrown back dead or dying into the sea.

Sign up to Hugh Fearnley-Whittingstall's Fish Fight, and learn more about sustainable fishing through the Marine Conservation Society's Fishing for our Future campaign.

Read more:
www.hardrainproject.com/food

Great White Shark caught in a deep-water driftnet, Santa Barbara, USA
© Tom Campbell/UNEP/Hard Rain Picture Library

Making waves

Simon King

One of the goals of the People's Postcode Lottery is
to raise awareness of the need to protect our oceans.
Through The Wildlife Trusts' Living Seas campaign,
it is supporting work locally and nationally to inspire
people about marine wildlife, convincing the UK
government to pass new laws to protect the sea and
carrying out vital research to help protect sharks,
dolphins, seals, corals and a host of rare and fragile
habitats.

Marine conservation brings a number of challenges.
It is very different from land-based action – we cannot
buy the seabed and declare it a reserve; we cannot
send teams of volunteers with cutters and bowsaws
to prune back a kelp forest; or let loose "herds" of
limpets to graze on an algal meadow.

Under 2009's Marine and Coastal Access Act,
the UK has committed itself to creating a network of
Marine Protected Areas (MPAs). MPAs are a proven
way of safeguarding important habitats and wildlife,
allowing nature and our seas to recover and thrive,
restricting human interventions and using the sea's
resources in an environmentally sound and sustainable
way.

Our seas and sea life have a remarkable capacity
to recover – but only if we give them a chance. Our
generation could go down in history as the one that
set our seas and oceans on the road to recovery.

Read more:
www.hardrainproject.com/making_waves
www.wildlifetrusts.org
www.postcodelottery.co.uk

Tompot blenny
© Paul Naylor/The Wildlife Trusts

Left:

Basking shark
© J.P. Trenque/The Wildlife Trusts

Reef with thongweed, south Devon
© Paul Naylor/The Wildlife Trusts

Grey seal
© Arthur Kingdon/The Wildlife Trusts

Okenia elegans sea slug
© Paul Naylor/The Wildlife Trusts

What'll you do now?

Breaking sustainable development down into topics – housing, energy, farming, etc. – makes the job sound big, but doable. We have the technology (mostly); the vision has been written out often enough. But what we see as good for the future of human civilization we do not necessarily see as good for our individual selves, right now. The wealthy who enjoy it like their carbon-based world, and they do not yet suffer from the carbon they spew out. We pretend to be negotiating toward a carbon-constrained world; we pretend we are making progress. We might just might pretend until it is too late.

Change, if it comes, will originate not through changing our technologies first, but through changing our minds: changing from judging success by ownership, switching from wanting more of everything to wanting the right amount, developing a sense of solidarity with those suffering the brunt of climate change. It is tough enough to dematerialize development; it is tougher to dematerialize our own mindsets.

But people who have done it – even those who have tried – have found it liberating, exhilarating and a lot of fun.

Here is our manifesto for a sustainable world. It's a checklist not to sign up to, but to live up to – and expand on.

Mark Edwards
Lloyd Timberlake

Tell us what you're doing to change your life and act in favour of the future:
www.hardrainproject.com/feedback

If you are not happy with your life, change it.

 Reconnect with nature.

 Walk the talk.

 Reuse. Repair. Restore. Recycle.

 Live better with less.

 Don't waste energy.

 Grow some of your food.

 Buy Fairtrade and shop at farmers' markets.

 Like to travel? Go to Africa and see the wildlife.

 Then visit the slums of Nairobi and work with NGOs at the sharp end of the debate.

 Arrange to absorb the carbon you burn.

 Write to politicians and business leaders and express your concerns.

 If you are part of the silent majority, now is the time to find your voice.

 The threats to our natural environment and very survival demand a radically new worldwide approach.

About Hard Rain Project

Hard Rain Project is a not-for profit company established to campaign for realistic solutions to global problems.

The original exhibition, *Hard Rain: Our headlong collision with nature*, has been seen by some 15 million people at over 100 venues around the world. One of the most successful photographic exhibitions ever created, it has attracted huge public and critical acclaim, along with the support and endorsement of political and environmental leaders across the world.

It highlights the interconnected problems of climate change, poverty, the wasteful use of resources, population expansion, habitat destruction and species loss.

Whole Earth? responds to requests by thousands of visitors and curators for an exhibition that presents solutions to the challenges set out in Hard Rain. It is designed to renew the ambitions for change in a large cross-section of the public and encourage political and business leaders to take bold, long-term decisions to secure our gains and avoid the disasters that appear increasingly imminent.

The Hard Rain Project website goes deeper into these issues, reporting on the complex interplay between people and the environment worldwide and presenting commentaries, features, fact files and images that can be downloaded free of charge for educational use.

Read more:
www.hardrainproject.com

Hard Rain at the Royal Botanic Gardens, Kew, summer 2011

Hard Rain shop

The Hard Rain book and DVD are available in good bookshops, at exhibition venues and from www.hardrainproject.com.

Book, DVD and print sales help fund public exhibitions that campaign for solutions to our interlinked problems.

Buy copies for your friends and colleagues and spread the story of the hard, hurting rain; what's causing it; how to stop it.

BOOK

In this extraordinarily powerful book – moving, delicate, cryptic, violent by turns – Edwards and Dylan remind us of how much is at stake.
Gerry McCarthy, **Sunday Times**

So why is Hard Rain so stunning and so moving, and why does it feel so right? Part of the answer, of course, lies in the quality of the visual images. But the thematic bundling of these images with Dylan's song could still seem gauche or exploitative were it not for two factors.

The most important of these is the sheer brilliance of the dialogue Edwards has created between the words and the images, the way they synthesise into some third form that combines the stillness of a picture with the urgency of a ballad. Edwards' conjunctions are so carefully and thoughtfully constructed that they enforce on the viewer a kind of tact that wards off mere voyeurism.
Fintan O'Toole, **Irish Times**

DVD

The Hard Rain DVD combines the images from Hard Rain with a rare live version of Bob Dylan performing "A Hard Rain's A-Gonna Fall" at Carnegie Hall, New York. It includes a voiceover commentary by Mark Edwards and is accompanied by "The Urgency of Now" by Lloyd Timberlake, an uncompromising essay that takes a critical look at the international response to the issues illustrated in this exhibition.

Hard Rain inspires me to try and stand again. To know that others share this bleakest outlook brings a ray of hope.

At first I thought that Dylan's lines should not be illustrated. I was wrong.
Christy Moore, **singer, songwriter and guitarist**

This disturbing, powerfully moving work is a masterpiece that summons up the ghosts of our past and a vision of the future that is ours to change. Regret and optimism make strange bedfellows, but great artists have always known this.
Tim Smit, **Chief Executive and co-founder, The Eden Project**

PRINTS

Photographs from the Hard Rain: Whole Earth? collection are available as digital prints from the Hard Rain shop. Visit the website, call or email with your enquiries.

www.hardrainproject.com/shop
+44 (0)20 8858 8307
shop@hardrainproject.com

Hard Rain documentary presentation

Support Hard Rain

The transformative power and real precision of poetry and the urgency of photography...

Mark Edwards' startlingly original presentation opens with Bob Dylan's "A Hard Rain's A-Gonna Fall". Photographs from around the world illustrate every line of Dylan's prophetic song, setting the scene for a moving and unforgettable exploration of the state of our planet at this critical time.

The issues illustrated in Hard Rain – "sad forests", "dead oceans", "Where the people are many and their hands are all empty", "Where hunger is ugly, where souls are forgotten" and the summation of our problems, climate change – are like pieces of a jigsaw puzzle that define the 21st century.

Edwards puts the puzzle together to show that there are not many problems but one problem with many solutions. The one problem: aligning human systems with natural systems.

We have the tools needed to decarbonize energy and surface transport. Experts are confident we could end the pockets of extreme poverty. We know how to bring down the birth rate. Scientists, engineers, and academics all over the world are working to develop the technologies and development strategies that will deliver a sustainable world. The final question is: is there the political will to reinvent the modern world so it's compatible with nature and human nature?

Hard Rain explores the values gap we need to cross if we are to have a secure future.

Hard Rain is one of the most powerful presentations I have ever seen – and it has a huge impact on audiences.
Jonathon Porritt, Founding Director, Forum for the Future

What is refreshing is that Mark doesn't paint the situation as hopeless. He highlights real changes governments, industry and individuals can make that are potentially highly effective.
Alex Ritson, Senior Editorial Advisor, BBC Global News

www.hardrainproject.com/talks

Hard Rain Project provides a platform for people from all walks of life to demonstrate support for sustainable development. Join us: run a marathon, donate a concert, host the exhibition and presentation, or donate funds to the project. All the money we raise is used to campaign for a sustainable future.

How can you help? Get in touch today.
Mark Edwards

+44 (0)20 8858 8307
mark@hardrainproject.com

About the contributors

Mark Edwards is one of the few environmental communicators to have personally witnessed the global issues that are defining the 21st century. Assignments for magazines, NGOs and United Nations agencies have taken him to over 150 countries. One of the most widely published photographers in the world, his pictures are in many international museums and private collections.

In 1985 he founded Still Pictures, the world's leading photo agency specializing in the environment, social issues and nature.

Previous environmental exhibitions include Focus on Your World, a display of 400 large prints at Heathrow Airport. It was seen by over 5 million travellers and judged the most popular attraction at the airport.

Mark has written several bestselling books on photography and co-authored *Changing Consciousness* with experimental physicist Professor David Bohm.

Lloyd Timberlake has reported on environment and development issues from more than 60 countries, and his articles have appeared in most of the world's major newspapers. He has written prize-winning books under his own name (*Africa in Crisis, Only One Earth, When the Bough Breaks*) and books for organizations such as the Brundtland Commission, the World Business Council for Sustainable Development and the UN Environment Programme. He recently advised President Obama's National Commission on the BP Deepwater Horizon Oil Spill and Offshore Drilling.

He has been a visiting academic fellow at Imperial College, London, and at New York University Law School. After graduating from Yale, he taught literature and chicken farming to members of Southern African revolutionary parties and served as honorary commandant of the Tanzanian Mounted Police Force. He has appeared as juggler onstage with the Rolling Stones and Bob Dylan, and in the House of Commons. He now lives in Washington DC and kayaks in the Chesapeake Bay.

The authors would like to thank the following people for their invaluable insights and comments:

Jonathon Porritt, co-founder of Forum for the Future, is an eminent writer, broadcaster and commentator on sustainable development and a special advisor to Hard Rain Project. His latest books are *Capitalism As If The World Matters, Globalism & Regionalism* and *Living Within Our Means.*
www.forumforthefuture.org

Fred Pearce is the environment and development consultant for the *New Scientist* and writes regularly for the *Guardian* and a wide variety of international media. His recent books include *The Climate Files, Peoplequake, When the Rivers Run Dry* and *Confessions of an Eco Sinner*.
authorsplace.co.uk/fred-pearce

Chris Goodall is the author of *Ten Technologies to Fix Energy and Climate, How to Live a Low-Carbon Life* and *The Green Guide for Business*, and on the advisory of board of the 10:10 emissions reduction campaign and other bodies. He is the editor of carboncommentary.com.
www.carboncommentary.com

Simon King, wildlife cameraman, author and presenter, is President of The Wildlife Trusts and trustee, patron or supporter of a dozen conservancy agencies in the UK and Africa. His latest books are *Wild Life: Amazing Animals, Extraordinary People, Astonishing Places* and *Shetland Diaries*.
www.wildlifetrusts.org
www.simonkingwildlife.com

Stewart Brand is best known as the editor of the *Whole Earth Catalog*. He is a co-founder of Global Business Network and the Long Now Foundation. His latest book is *Whole Earth Discipline*.
web.me.com/stewartbrand

Julie Hill is an associate and former Director of Green Alliance, working on projects including waste, producer responsibility, procurement and product policy. She is the author of *The Secret Life of Stuff: A Manual for a New Material World*.
www.green-alliance.org.uk

Harriet Lamb is the Executive Director of the Fairtrade Foundation and a former Head of Campaigns at the World Development Movement. She is the author of *Fighting the Banana Wars and Other Fairtrade Battles*.
www.fairtrade.org.uk

Additional photography

We are indebted to all the photographers whose work is included in this exhibition. Their contribution to the debate is often overlooked in the media but it is their skill at capturing life at the sharp end that keeps the issues on the agenda.

UNEP Archive

The UNEP Archive grew out of four photography competitions organized by UNEP. The invitation to participate was simple: comment on the environment through the medium of photography. Camera owners from every continent and almost every country responded with over 100,000 images. They reflect the concerns of ordinary people all over the world rather than those of environmental experts. The men, women and children who took the photographs see them as a means to support action to bring real, long-term environmental security to people around the world. The collection was edited by Mark Edwards and is housed in the Hard Rain Picture Library.

Hard Rain Picture Library

Browse and download pictures from this exhibition and discover thousands more. This archive is designed to support charities that respond to the challenges highlighted in Hard Rain. World-class photographs are available at affordable rates, and many of the pictures are free for educational use.
www.hardrainproject.com/hrpl

Still Pictures and partners

Hard Rain and *Whole Earth?* also include many images from the collections of Still Pictures and its partner agencies including Biosphoto.
www.stillpictures.com
www.biosphoto.com

"What'll you do now?" images: © Mark Edwards/Hard Rain Picture Library; A. Detrich/UNEP/Hard Rain Picture Library; Mark Edwards/Hard Rain Picture Library; Thomas Wolke/ UNEP; Mark Edwards/Hard Rain Picture Library; photographer unknown; Florence/UNEP; Ron Giling/Lineair; Brunner/UNEP; Mark Edwards/Hard Rain Picture Library; Mark Edwards/ Hard Rain Picture Library; A. Zhdanov/UNEP; Mark Edwards/ Hard Rain Picture Library; Chris Steele-Perkins/Magnum

The photographs in the Rainforest Concern Forest Credits section are reproduced by kind permission of Murray Cooper.
www.murraycooperphoto.com

The views expressed are not necessarily those of the copyright holders

How this book was made

Pureprint Group is Hard Rain Project's print partner. The UK's leading environmental printer, the company's quality and sustainability standards have been recognized by over 60 industry awards in the last 10 years.

This book is printed using *pure***print**® environmental print technology on FSC® certified Revive 50:50 Silk, a recycled paper containing 50% recovered fibre and 50% virgin fibre manufactured at a mill certified with ISO 14001 environmental management standard. The pulp used in this book is bleached using an Elemental Chlorine-Free process, the inks are made from vegetable-based oils, and an average of 99% of all waste associated with production is recycled.

Pureprint is a CarbonNeutral Company and was awarded the Queen's Award for Enterprise: Sustainable Development in 2003 and 2008.

Pureprint Group

www.pureprint.com

Forest Credits
by Rainforest Concern

Main image:
Cloud forest on the western slopes of the Andes,
Maquipucuna Reserve, Ecuador

All photographs © Murray Cooper

Top row, left to right:
Choco toucan
Purple-bibbed whitetip hummingbird
Sunbittern feeding frog to chicks
White-necked jacobin feeding on flower nectar
Golden-naped tanager
Crab spider on native *passiflora* flower

Bottom row, left to right:
Long-wattled umbrellabird
Caligo, or Owl butterfly
Transverse Anole eye
Dalceridae moth caterpillar
Fringed Leaf Frog
Saturniidae moth caterpillar

Rainforest Concern's Forest Credits carbon offsetting programme is based on halting the destruction of natural forests, in particular the native rainforests of Latin America.

Offsetting is a way for all of us to take action on climate change by taking responsibility for our carbon footprint and supporting emission-reduction projects. CO_2 emissions and other greenhouse gases occur everywhere and all the time from everyday life, such as driving, flying, industry and agriculture, and heating our homes and offices.

Standing native forests are a very important store of carbon and if they are destroyed much of this carbon will be released into the atmosphere. It is therefore essential to protect them.

Responsible offsetting means reducing your emissions first, then balancing your remaining emissions through the purchase of offsets, which are measured in tonnes of carbon dioxide equivalent (tCO_2e).

Forest Credits concentrates on areas of exceptional and threatened biodiversity in Central and South America. Our vision is long-term,

and apart from securing the forest, we help local communities understand the importance of their natural environment and find alternative sustainable income now and in the future, for the continuing safeguard of these forests.
Peter Bennett, Executive Director and Founder, Rainforest Concern

Read more:
www.hardrainproject.com/forest_credits
www.rainforestconcern.org

Sign up to Forest Credits:
www.forestcredits.org.uk

Registered Charity No. 1028947

The carbon emissions from Hard Rain Project have been fully offset through Forest Credits

Hard Rain project partners

Enabling partners

The Swedish International Development Cooperation Agency (Sida) has funded a two-year tour of this exhibition to principal cities throughout Sweden, featuring customized content that illustrates Swedish sustainable development projects at home and in the majority world.
www.sida.se

People's Postcode Lottery has raised over £16 million for good causes across Britain which benefit both people and the planet. The Lottery supports its charity partners' commitments to protect the marine environment, highlight the fragile nature of our oceans and campaign for better fishing practices.
www.postcodelottery.co.uk

(*see previous spread*)
www.rainforestconcern.org
www.forestcredits.org.uk

Network for Social Change
www.thenetworkforsocialchange.org.uk

www.britishcouncil.org

Founding partners

UNEP

The UN Environmental Programme (UNEP) coordinates United Nations environmental activities, assisting developing countries in implementing environmentally sound policies and encouraging sustainable development.
www.unep.org

The enthusiasm and support of our original partner venue, Eden Project, opened the way to display Hard Rain at outdoor venues on every continent. Eden Project is an inspirational UK visitor attraction, and delivers projects worldwide that benefit the environment and act as a focus for social and economic regeneration.
www.edenproject.com

COLUMBIA

Hard Rain Project is deeply grateful for the continuing support of Columbia Records, London and Sony/ATV Music Publishing Ltd.
www.columbia.co.uk

Educational outreach

The Environmental Association for Universities and Colleges is the sustainability champion for Further and Higher Education in the UK.
www.eauc.org.uk

Working with young people, graduates, businesses and communities for a sustainable future.
www.changeagents.org.uk

The national voice of students.
www.nus.org.uk

Simple solutions to save lives.
www.practicalaction.org

BGCI
Plants for the Planet

Botanic Gardens Conservation International is the world's greatest force for plant conservation.
www.bgci.org